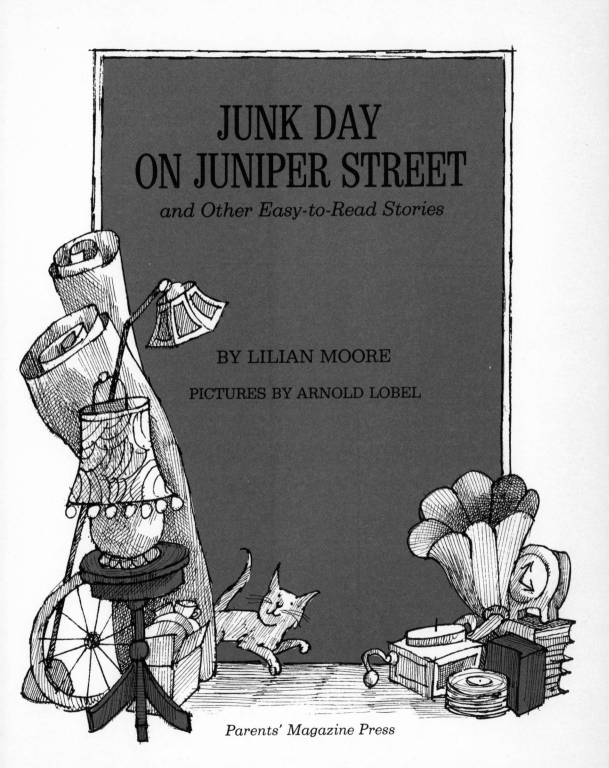

JUNK DAY
ON JUNIPER STREET

and Other Easy-to-Read Stories

BY LILIAN MOORE

PICTURES BY ARNOLD LOBEL

Parents' Magazine Press

For Rose and Gerald
to read to Noah and Freedom

Contents

Junk Day on Juniper Street

How did it begin?

No one on Juniper Street can really say.

Benny and Jenny say it began in their house.

Debby says it really began in her backyard.

But Davy thinks his father started it all.

One morning Davy's father was reading his newspaper.

"Take a look at this!" he said to Davy's mother.

> DO YOU HAVE JUNK
> AROUND *YOUR* HOUSE?
> THEN IT'S CLEAN-UP TIME!

"Do we have junk?" asked Davy.

"Well . . ." said his mother.

Later, Davy's mother and Debby's mother
met in the backyard.

Davy's mother said, "Look at this."
And she showed her the newspaper.

DO YOU HAVE JUNK
AROUND *YOUR* HOUSE?
THEN IT'S CLEAN-UP TIME!

"Do *we* have junk?" asked Debby.

"Hmmmmmm . . ." said her mother.

Later, some mothers met to have coffee.
They met at Benny and Jenny's house.

"Did you see this?" asked Debby's mother.
And she showed them the newspaper.

Jenny asked, "Do *we* have junk?"

All the mothers began to laugh.

"We all have junk," they said.
"Lots and lots of junk!"

Then someone said, "Let's do it! Let's have
a Take-Out-All-the-Junk-Day!"

So Juniper Street had a Junk Day.

It was a big clean-up time in every house.

Mothers and fathers and children walked
from one room to the next, saying, "Do we need
this anymore? Do we want to keep *that?*"

Then everyone began to put out the junk
—the old chairs
—the old tables
—the old toys and pictures and books.

And every time they looked around the house,
people saw more junk to take out
—an old lamp
—a yellow bird cage
—a big old rocking chair.

Soon there was a pile of junk outside every house on Juniper street.

Davy's father looked up and down the street.

"Wow!" he said. "We will need a big truck to take all this away!"

Benny's father called up the junk man.

"We have lots of junk on Juniper Street," he told the man. "You will need a big truck to take it all."

"I have a big truck," said the junk man. "But I can't come today. I will come for your junk in the morning."

"Don't forget," said Benny's father. "A big truck."

All day, people walked past the piles of junk on Juniper Street.

It was hard to go by without taking a good look.

Davy stopped outside Debby's house.

"Say, there's a good wheel!" he cried.

"I need a wheel like that for my wagon.
May I have it?"

Debby's mother said yes.

Later Debby's father stopped to look
at the junk outside Davy's house.

He saw an old tool box.

"Why, it's just what I need!" he said.

"Take it!" said Davy's father.

Soon many people were saying, "Take it!"

Jenny's mother saw a little table she liked.

"I need a little table
in the little room," she said.

Debby's mother found a big hatbox
in the junk outside Jenny's house.

"I can keep my big red hat in this,"
she said happily.

Jenny saw a doll bed across the street.

She took her doll Amanda across the street
and put her in the bed.

"It's just like the three bears," she told
Amanda, "not too big, not too little,
but just right!"

So Jenny asked for the doll bed.

By this time everyone was visiting the junk
next door and the junk across the street.

A man picked up a lamp.

"Do you call *this* junk?" he said.
"I can fix this lamp in no time."
And off he went with it.

An old lady took home the yellow bird cage.

"Now I can get a bird!" she cried.

Someone was happy to find a window box.

"I'll paint it green," he said,
"and put in some red geraniums."

Someone saw an old picture of the sea.

"I lived by the sea when I was a boy," he said,
and he took the picture home.

By the time the sun went down, there was
no more junk on Juniper street
—well, almost none.

One thing was left.

It was a big rocking chair.

Many people stopped to look at it
but everyone said, "Too big!"

So there it stood.

The next morning a big truck came
down Juniper street.

"Oh my," said Benny's father. "We forgot
to tell the junk man not to come!"

The truck came slowly down the street
and stopped.

The man who got out of the truck
was big, too.

He looked up and down the street.

All he saw was the rocking chair.
He walked over and looked at it.
Then he sat down and began to rock.
"At last!" he said happily.
"A big rocking chair!"
Then he put the chair on his truck,
and off he went with all the junk
on Juniper Street.

Duckling Number Five

He was a little dog.

His name was Pepper.

And this was the first time he had been
on a farm.

The farm was full of surprises.

"Woof! What's that?" said Pepper,
and he ran after a bee.

He stood under a tree and *pop!*
Something hit him.

He looked up at the tree and said,
"Woof! So that's where apples come from!"

He ran to the big red barn
and looked inside.

He saw a horse and a cow.

Oh, thought Pepper, this is where they live.
Then he ran into the barn.

"Hello!" he said to the cow. "Here I am!
I'm going to live on the farm, too!"

"Little Gray Dog," said the cow. "Do stop
running around me. You make me quite dizzy."

Pepper ran over to the horse.

"Hello!" he said. "Here I am! I'm going
to live on the farm, too!"

"Little Gray Dog," said the horse. "Do stop jumping all over my hay. That's my supper."

Next, Pepper ran out to the barnyard.

There he saw a mother duck and her ducklings.

"Quack! Quack!" the mother duck was saying. "Let's try again. One—Two—Three—Four —Oh! Oh! Where is Number Five? Where is my Duckling Number Five?"

Pepper was happy to help.

"I'll find him for you!" he said, and off he ran.

Pepper found the little yellow duckling
walking down the road.

"Woof!" he said. "Your mother is looking
for you. Come home."
And he showed the duckling
the way to the barnyard.

Mother Duck was very happy.

"Thank you, Little Gray Dog," she said.
"Number Five keeps getting lost!"

"I will take care of him today," said Pepper.

It was hard to take care of Duckling
Number Five.

Very soon he was lost again.

Pepper looked for him on the road.

He called, "Number Five! Number Five!"
No duckling.

Where was he?

Pepper sat down by the haystack to think.

"Peep!"
What was that?

Pepper looked around.

There was Duckling Number Five
looking at him from the haystack.

"Woof!" said Pepper. "It's a good thing
I know where to look for you."
And he took the duckling back to the barnyard.

But soon the duckling was lost again.

Pepper looked on the road.

He looked in the haystack.

He called, "Number Five! Where are you?"

No duckling.

Then he saw something funny.

He saw the farmer's hat in the grass,

and it was moving.

Pepper ran after the hat.

But the hat began to run.

Pepper ran faster.

The hat ran faster, too.

Then Pepper got hold of the hat.

And there, under the hat, was the duckling.

"You will not get away from me again!"
said Pepper.

After that, Pepper stayed right by the duckling.

When Mother Duck took a walk, there they were

—Mother Duck

—Duckling One

—Duckling Two

—Duckling Three

—Duckling Four

—Duckling Five and

—Pepper!

Then Pepper ran after a butterfly,
and Duckling Number Five was lost again.

Pepper looked up and down the road.

He looked all around the haystack.

He looked for the farmer's hat. (This time
the farmer was under the hat.)

And then at last he saw the duckling.
He was walking to the pond!

"No!" cried Pepper. "Don't go there!"
But the Duckling went right on,
and before Pepper got to him, *splash!*
Number Five was in the water.

"Oh!" cried Pepper. "I can't swim!
I must get help!"

The little gray dog ran all the way
back to the barn.

The cow was eating.

"Cow!" cried Pepper. "Come as fast
as you can! A duckling fell into the pond!"

The cow looked at Pepper and went on eating.

How can she eat at a time like this?
thought Pepper, and he ran to the horse.

The horse was sleeping.

"Horse!" cried Pepper. "Come as fast
as you can! A duckling fell into the pond!"

The horse looked at Pepper
and went back to sleep.

How can he sleep at a time like this?
thought the little dog.

Pepper took a rope from the barn,
and started back to the pond.

It was hard to run with the rope.
Pepper fell under it and over it.
But he did not give up.

He got to the pond fast.

Then he stopped and looked.

Mother Duck was swimming in the pond,
and behind her were the ducklings
—One
—Two
—Three
—Four

—and FIVE!

"Quack!" said Mother Duck.

"Peep!" called Number Five to Pepper.

"Woof!" Pepper called back.

The farm was just *full* of surprises!

A Fish Story

Kenny was angry.

His father and his brother Jim were
going fishing—*without him!*

"I want to go, too!" Kenny cried.

"Not today, Kenny," said his father.
"You can come next time."

Sadly, Kenny saw his father and brother
go off in the car.

"Go fishing with Andy," said Kenny's mother.
"You can fish in Raccoon Pond."

"Raccoon Pond!" cried Kenny. "That little old
—old fish bowl!"

"I'll make you the same picnic lunch I made
for Daddy and Jim," said his mother,
"with chocolate cake!"

It's not the same, thought Kenny.
Not like going fishing
with his father and his brother.
But Andy and he might catch some fish.
Say, they might catch more fish
than Daddy and Jim!

Kenny took the picnic lunch
and went to call for Andy.

"Fishing at Raccoon Pond!" yelled Andy.
"Oh boy! Let's go!"

Andy had just moved from the city,
and he thought *everything* was fun.

"Just don't talk when we fish," Kenny said.
"We have to catch a *lot* of fish today."

"Why?" asked Andy as they walked
down the road to the pond.

"Just because," said Kenny.

By the time they got to Raccoon Pond,
Andy was hungry.

"But we just had breakfast," said Kenny.

Then he thought of the chocolate cake,
and he began to feel hungry, too.

So right after breakfast, they sat down
to eat lunch. Kenny ate the cake first
so he would have room for it.

Andy looked out at the pond.

"Why do they call this Raccoon Pond?"
he asked.

"There are lots of raccoons around here,"
said Kenny. "And they like this pond."

"Do you ever see them?" asked Andy.

"Oh, yes," said Kenny. "We have a raccoon
that comes to our back door all the time.
He got into our house once."

31

After eating everything they had,
the boys walked around the pond.
They found a good place to fish.
Then they threw in their lines
and sat very still.

Once Kenny thought he had a fish.
But it was nothing.

Once Andy thought he had a fish.
But it was nothing.

Andy found it hard to sit still so long.

"Say, there's a frog!" he yelled.
"Let's catch it!"

So that's what they did.
Then they fished again.
Once Kenny thought he had a fish.
Once Andy thought he had a fish.
But it was nothing.

They looked for frogs again.

Then Andy said, "I'm hungry!"

"Let's fish once more before we go,"
said Kenny.

So once more they threw in their lines
and sat very still.

All at once there was a pull on Kenny's line.
A good hard pull.

"I've got something!" he yelled. "A big one!"

"Pull it in!" cried Andy. "Pull hard!"

Kenny pulled and pulled. But his line
did not come out of the water.

"Say, you must have a whale!" cried Andy.

Kenny pulled again. This time he fell way back, and his line was free.

"What's that thing on your hook?" asked Andy. "What kind of fish is *that?*"

"That's no fish," said Kenny. "It's just some junk my hook pulled in."

"But what is it?" asked Andy.

Then Kenny took a good look at the thing he had fished out of the pond.

He pulled it off the hook and cried, "Come on! Let's go home!"

They got to Kenny's house just as his father and Jim were getting out of the car.

His mother came to the door to meet them.

"Hello, all you fishermen!" she called. "How was the fishing today?"

"Not so good," said Jim sadly. "Look." He held up three little fish.

"Guess what *I* fished out of Raccoon Pond!" cried Kenny. And he held it up.

"No!" said his father.

"No fooling!" said his brother.

"Oh, Kenny!" cried his mother.
"My good gold bracelet!"

Kenny thought she was going to cry,
but she gave him a big hug.

"Raccoon Pond!" said Kenny's father.
"So that's where it was!
That raccoon took the bracelet
and dropped it there."

"What a fisherman you are, Kenny!"
said Jim, laughing.

Kenny's mother hugged him again.

"Anybody can catch a fish," she said happily.
"It took Kenny to pull in my gold bracelet."

The House that Nobody Wanted

There was once a little house that stood
on a hill.

It was an old house—very old and very gray.
It had gray doors and gray windows, gray walls
and a gray fence.

A little old man and a little old woman
lived in this house.

And they had lived there for a long time.

The old man and the old woman did not
go out much. But one fine day they
made up their minds to visit their friends.

So they got into their little old car
and rode away. They rode uphill and downhill
and then uphill and downhill again.

And at last they saw the house of their friends.
It was a little red house
with white doors and windows,
and all around it flowers and green things
were growing.

The little old man and the little old woman
had a good time with their friends.

Then they got into their little old car
and went home. They rode uphill and downhill,
then uphill and downhill again.

And at last they came to their own house.

"My!" said the old woman. "Our house
is *very* gray, isn't it?"

"And there is nothing green to see
when we look out," said the old man.

"Old man, let's sell this house!"
said the old woman. "Then we can buy
a pretty house!"

". . . with grass and flowers growing
around it!" said the old man.

So the little old man and the little old woman
tried to sell their house.

First a man came to look.

"No," he said. "This house is too gray
for me. I like a red house."

And he went away.

"Oh dear!" said the little old woman.

"Let's paint the house red," said the old man.
"Then maybe the next one will buy it."

So the little old man and the little old woman
painted the house red.

Soon after, a woman came to look.

"I like a house that has white windows
and white doors," she said. "I like a white fence
and a white gate, too." And she went away.

So the little old man and the little old woman painted the windows white. Then they painted the doors and the gate and the fence white, too.

Soon after that, a man and a woman came to see the house. They liked the outside.

"But it is so gray inside," said the woman.

And they went away.

So this time the little old man and the little old woman painted the walls inside the house. They painted some walls yellow and some walls blue.

Soon another man came to see the house.

"This is a pretty house," he said.

"But I am looking for a home with a garden."

And he, too, went away.

The old man and the old woman
began to work on a garden.

Soon green grass was growing.

Then one day there were flowers—red
and purple and yellow—growing
all around the house.

"Now," said the old woman.
"Someone will want to buy this house!
Then at last we can buy the house *we* want."

The old man looked around.

"Old woman," he said. "What kind of house
do we want?"

"Well," she said. "We want a pretty house."

"Painted inside and out?" he asked.

"Oh yes!" said the old woman.

"With grass and flowers growing around it?"
asked the old man.

"Oh yes!" said the little old woman.
The old man laughed.
"Look around, old woman!" he told her.
So the little old woman looked around.
She saw a red house with white windows
and doors, a white fence and a white gate, too.
Inside the house she saw bright
yellow and blue walls.
Outside she saw grass and flowers growing.
"Well!" she said, surprised.
"This is a pretty house, isn't it?"
"This is just the house we want!"
said the old man.
So the little old man and the little old woman
went right on living in the little old house
on the hill.
Only it wasn't a little gray house anymore.

The Peanut Butter Sandwich

Janey's mother was making her school lunch.

"May I have a peanut butter sandwich?"
said Janey. "Susie had a peanut butter sandwich
yesterday."

Janey's mother made a peanut butter sandwich.

"Susie had an apple, too," said Janey.

Janey's mother put an apple
into the lunch box.

"Susie had a big cookie," said Janey.

Janey's mother put a big cookie
next to the apple.

Then she said, "Now tell me, Janey.
Who is Susie?"

"She's a new girl in my class," said Janey,
"and she sits next to me and we are going
to be best friends!"

Then it was time to go.

Janey ran down the street.

She stopped for the red light. There was
her dog Brownie waiting for the light, too.

"Go home, Brownie!" said Janey.

Brownie looked sad, but he went home.

Janey met Susie as she came out of her house.

"Look, Janey!" said Susie. "There's a dog
behind you!"

It was Brownie again.

"Go home!" said Janey. "Go right home!"

Brownie looked sad, but he went home.

Janey had a good day at school.

And lunch was fun because she and Susie
had the same things to eat.

"Let's do this again!" said Susie.

So the next morning Janey went off to school
with the very same kind of lunch.

Brownie was right behind her,
but she did not see him.

He waited until she crossed the street.

Then he crossed.

He waited until she walked down the street
with Susie.

Then he walked down the street.

When Janey walked into the schoolyard,
the children called, "Look, Janey!
There's a dog behind you!"

"Brownie!" cried Janey. "Go home!
Go right home!"

Brownie looked sad, but he went home.

The next morning Janey's mother said,
"How about a meat sandwich
for lunch today?"

"Oh, please!" said Janey. "Can't I have
a peanut butter sandwich?"

"And an apple and a big cookie,"
said her mother, "just like Susie?"

So once more Janey went to school
with a peanut butter sandwich.

She did not see Brownie behind her.

He waited until she crossed the street.

Then he crossed.

He waited until she walked down the street.

Then he walked down the street.

This time he waited until the children went inside.

Then Brownie ran into the schoolyard.

Janey was in Room 6.

Miss Hill was her teacher.

She was telling the class a story.

All at once the door opened.

A little brown nose poked into the room —then a little brown face, then a little brown dog.

"Miss Hill!" the children cried. "Look! There's a dog!"

"Brownie!" said Janey. "What are you doing here?"

"Is that your dog, Janey?" asked Miss Hill.

Janey told the teacher about Brownie.

"He wants to come to school with me," said Janey. "I don't understand it."

"Well," said Miss Hill, "if he is a good dog, he may stay in school this morning."

It was fun to have Brownie in the room.

The class did number work.

"Brownie," said Miss Hill. "What is 1 and 1?"

"Woof! Woof!" said Brownie,
and everybody laughed.

The class took out their books.

Miss Hill showed Brownie a picture of a dog.

"Brownie," she said, "what is this?"

"Woof! Woof!" said Brownie, and everybody laughed again.

Then the children began to draw pictures, and Brownie went to the back of the room.

He was very, very quiet.

All at once a boy cried, "Look at Brownie!"

Everyone in the class turned around to look.
"He's eating!" a girl cried.
That's just what Brownie was doing.
He was eating Janey's peanut butter sandwich.
"Oh!" cried Janey. "My lunch!"
Brownie looked very happy as he ate
the last of the peanut butter sandwich.
"My peanut butter sandwich!" cried Janey.
"So that's what Brownie wanted all the time."

The next morning Janey said to her mother,
"May I have a cheese and jelly sandwich today?"

"Like Susie?" asked her mother.

"Yes," said Janey. "And a banana
and a carrot, too?"

"I know," said her mother. "Just like Susie."

As Janey said good-bye, Brownie came
running to her.

Janey's mother laughed. "Are you going
to school today, too, Brownie?" she asked.

Sniff! Sniff!

Brownie walked all around Janey's lunch box.
Sniff! Sniff!

He walked away.

"No peanut butter!" he seemed to be saying.
"What kind of lunch is *that?*"

No-Go the Donkey

Once upon a time there was a little boy
and a little donkey, and they lived
in a little town.

The town was on the side of a hill.

The boy was called Marco.

And the donkey's name was No-Go.

It was a good name for this donkey.
For he went only where *he* wanted to go.
He went only when *he* wanted to go.

At last the people in the town said,
"You are a lazy, good-for-nothing donkey!
Go away!"

No one wanted to give him a home.

No one wanted to keep him anymore.

So the little donkey went up into the hills
to live.

Sometimes he came down into the town.

Then people cried, "Go back to the hills,
you No-Go of a donkey!"

What did the little boy Marco have to do
with the little donkey?

Nothing—at first.

The people in the town were poor,
and they had to work long and hard.
But Marco saw that sometimes the men
got on donkeys and rode up into the hills.

One day Marco said, "Mama, the men are
riding off again! Where are they going?"

"Ah," said Marco's mother. "They will
not give up. They are still looking
for the treasure."

"The treasure!" cried Marco.
"What treasure?"

"They say there is silver in our hills,"
his mother told him. "But no one can find it."

"Is it silver money?" asked Marco.
"Is that the treasure?"

"No," said his mother. "The silver is not
money. It is in the very rocks of our hills."

"What good is it then?" asked Marco.

"If the men once find the silver,"
said his mother, "they can take it out
of the rock. Ah, then no one in our town
will be poor anymore."

"Oh, Mama!" cried Marco. "I want to ride
up in the hills, too! I wish I had a donkey
—*my* donkey!"

Marco's mother began to laugh.

"Look!" she said. "Here comes a donkey
for you. Here is that no-good No-Go."

Yes, there was No-Go again.

The children were calling, "Go away,
lazy No-Go. Go away!"

But the little donkey went when *he* wanted to go.
Now he stood still and looked around.

As if he is looking for a friend,
thought Marco. He jumped up.

"Mama," he said, "may I take No-Go
back to the hills—a little way?"

"If you can," said his mother, laughing.
"No one takes No-Go anywhere."

Marco did not really take No-Go back.
He just talked to him and walked with him
a little way up into the hills.

The next morning Marco had a surprise.
No-Go was at his door.

Marco gave the donkey a big hug.

"Oh, No-Go!" he cried. "Will you really
be my donkey? I will not try to make you go
where you do not want to go. I will not try
to make you go when you do not want to go."

No-Go looked at the boy as if to say,
"Do you mean that?"

And after that they went for a ride
in the hills every day.

Marco did not mean to forget what he had said.

It was just that one day he looked
way up at the hills and said to the donkey,
"Go this way."

The little donkey stood still.

"Come on, No-Go," said Marco.
"Go to the right here."

No-Go went to the left.

"No, no!" cried Marco. "To the right!"

No-Go went on walking to the left.

"No!" cried Marco again. "That way, I say!"

No-Go stopped.

He stopped so fast that Marco
went right over the donkey . . .
and onto the ground with a *bump*.
He had to keep his eyes closed,
for he seemed to be spinning around.

Then Marco opened his eyes.

But he closed them at once.

For it still seemed that he was spinning
and the rocks around him were
full of dancing lights.

He opened his eyes again.

The rocks were still shining.

Marco got up. He walked to the bright rocks
and put out his hand.

And he knew.

He knew it was silver shining in the rocks.
Marco ran to the donkey and gave him a hug.
"Oh, No-Go!" he said. "You have found it!
You have found the treasure in the hills!
How everyone will love you now!"
The little donkey looked at Marco.
He seemed to say, "But no more nonsense!"
Then the boy and the donkey went back
to the town to tell what they had found.
And guess who led the way!

Grown-Ups Are Funny

Grown-ups are funny, thought Ramon.
It is so nice here and they want to move
to an apartment house.

"Do not be sad, Ramon," said his mother.

"But I like it here in Grandfather's house,"
said Ramon.

"You will like the apartment house, too,"
said his father. "It is nice and big
and there are many, many apartments."

Then how will I find *my* apartment?
thought Ramon.

"Many people live there!" said his Aunt Rosa,
and she looked very happy.

But what if they are all grown-ups?
thought Ramon.

What if they are all *girls?*

Soon they did move—Ramon and his father
and mother and his Aunt Rosa.

It was a sad day for Ramon. When he said
good-bye to Grandfather's cat, Big Pedro,
he wanted to cry.

Ramon put his arms around the cat and said,
"Good-bye, Big Pedro. I love you."

Big Pedro said, "Mew!" and rubbed himself
against Ramon.

The day they moved was a day of surprises, too.

The apartment house had five floors.

Ramon's apartment was 3A.

I can find that, thought Ramon. All I do is
go to floor three and look for 3A.

The best surprise was the children.

Lots of children!

Girls *and* boys!

Soon Ramon got to know them.

Jimmy lived on the top floor in Apartment 5B.

Leon lived in Apartment 4C.

Johnny and his sister Lola lived
right next door to Ramon.

And the twins, Sara and Sammy,
lived right under Ramon
in Apartment 2A.

There was always someone
to play with.

Every day Ramon ran up to the
top floor and called for Jimmy.

Then Jimmy and Ramon ran
downstairs to call for Leon.

Then Leon and Jimmy and Ramon
ran downstairs to call
for Johnny and Lola.

They all went downstairs to call
for the twins.

And then they ran out to play.

Mr. Carlos took care of the apartment house.

He lived downstairs with a big gray cat
that he called Missus.

Some of the children were afraid of the big cat.

When Ramon saw her, he thought of Big Pedro
and put his arms around her.

The cat said, "Mew," and rubbed
herself against Ramon.

After that, Ramon and Missus and Mr. Carlos
were friends. Sometimes Mr. Carlos let Ramon
feed the cat.

Ramon loved Missus.

"I wish you were my cat!" he told her.

One morning, Ramon's mother took him
to the store to buy sneakers.

Ramon wanted to play in his new white sneakers
right away.

As soon as they got home, he ran upstairs
and rang the bell of Apartment 5B.

"Hello, Ramon," said Jimmy's mother.
"Jimmy went down to call for Leon."

Ramon ran downstairs and rang the bell
of Apartment 4C.

"Hello, Ramon," said Leon's mother.
"Leon and Jimmy went to call for Johnny
and Lola."

Johnny and Lola had called for the twins.
But the twins were not at home now.

Ramon ran outside. He walked around
looking for his friends.

No one was to be seen.

That's funny, thought Ramon.

Where is everybody?

He did not feel like playing
in his new sneakers now.

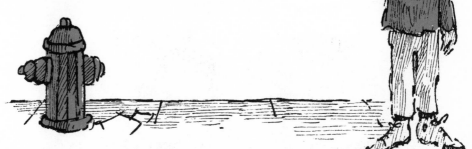

He sat down on the steps of his house,
and that was where Mr. Carlos found him.

"Hello," said Mr. Carlos.
"What are you doing *here,* Ramon?"

"I came out to find somebody to play with,"
said Ramon, "but I can't find *anybody!*"

"They are all looking at something,"
said Mr. Carlos.

Ramon jumped up.

"Looking at what?" he cried.

"Come and see."

Mr. Carlos went downstairs with Ramon
right behind him.

Then Ramon saw his friends.
And he saw what they were looking at.

Missus was lying in a box,
and right beside her were three tiny kittens.

"Oh!" cried Ramon, and he ran to the box.

"Look at the little white one!" said Jimmy. "That's the one I like best."

"I like the black one," said Leon.

"And you, Ramon?" asked Mr. Carlos.

Ramon looked at the little gray kitten and thought of Big Pedro.

"That one," he said.

"How little they are!" said Sara.

"They will grow fast," said Mr. Carlos. "Soon they will be running into everything. After that, I have to give them away."

"Give them away!" cried the children.

"I can't keep four cats," said Mr. Carlos. "The black one is for my friend down the street. The white one is for my sister."

Ramon looked at the little gray kitten.

"And that one?" he asked.

Mr. Carlos laughed.

"Missus says that kitten is for Ramon."

That night Ramon told his mother and father
and Aunt Rosa all about the kitten.

"I will call him Little Pedro," said Ramon.

"I will see Big Pedro soon," said Aunt Rosa.

"I am going back to Grandfather's house to live."

Ramon looked at her in surprise.

"I do not like it here," said his aunt.

"An apartment house is too big.

Too many people!"

Ramon shook his head.

It is so nice here,
he thought, and Aunt Rosa
is moving away.
Grown-ups
are funny.